Dear Reader,

Our hope is that these tools help you in becoming the best version of YOU.

We all struggle with obstacles. But if we know the skill set which attacks adversity, then we stand a better chance of reaching our highest dreams.

Sincerely,
Kobe Nhin

ISBN 978-1-7338627-4-5 (paperback)
ISBN 978-1-7338627-5-2 (ebook)

Cataloging in Publication Data Library of Congress Control number: 2019906947
First published May 2019

www.kobenhin.com

HOW TO WIN THE WORLD CUP IN PAJAMAS

This book is dedicated to kids all over the world
who would like to develop their mental toughness and grit.

Grow Grit Press

Hi, my name is Emma.
The World Cup is very hard to win,
but I've won it many times in my pajamas.

And that's why, I'm giving you

5 tools on how to win the

World Cup in pajamas.

TOOL 1: Work on developing **Grit**.

Winning the World Cup starts years
before the actual championship.

Write down some goals.
This keeps you motivated.
Then, practice, practice, practice.

And when the going gets tough,
reach within to find your inner strength.

TOOl 2: It's good to perform your usual Rituals.

The morning of the World Cup,
be sure to eat your regular breakfast.

Going outside to play can
help keep your mind relaxed.

This makes you comfortable.
And boosts your confidence.

Visualize the field.

Smell the turf below your feet.
Dribble the ball down the field.

Feel it listen to your every command.

If you make mistakes, no worries. Stay carefree by focusing on your performance and not the outcome.

TOOl 4: Use Mantras
like, "Work hard!" or "Right here!"

Take some deep breaths like a dragon.
Inhale for 3 seconds. Exhale for 3 seconds.

And think of your strategy for the next pass.
Doing this helps to keep you focused.

TOOl 5: Keep up the
Positive Body Language.

Bounce up and down on your toes.
Stay confident and upbeat.
Have good posture.

Now, fire past your opponent.
And take your shot.
Watch it curl in.

Can you hear the crowd roar?

Relish in your newfound victory.
Thank those who have helped you.

If you think of any more tools, write them down.
I'm going to get ready for soccer practice.

Grow Grit Press Mission Statement

Encourage a growth mindset: We believe it is important for kids to develop intrinsic motivation and autonomy through the development of long-term goals. Setting our sights on performance goals, rather than outcome goals provide a basis for grit and perseverance. We hope these books give children a love for battling new challenges and that they grow up eager to explore what this big, beautiful world has to offer.

Cultivate kids' self-confidence: We believe it is important for kids to learn how to practice positive self-talk. The more they understand that even mistakes and failures teach us, the more they can focus on celebrating their journey, mistakes and all. Our books will teach kids to be courageous enough to take risks and trust that the dots will someday connect. We want to teach kids how it feels to be scared and brave all at once, and how to move past fear and learn to jump.

Increase kids' focus and attention: We all get side-tracked and that's why it's important to have rituals to reset oneself. Our hope is that these stories will help kids get back on track and focus on the task at hand. Life itself is overwhelming. We want to help kids see that everyone faces hurdles and that we can stay focused with habits and mantras.

Develop perseverance and grit: Setbacks and failures teach us how to be graceful in the face of adversity. The books aim to encourage diligence and a hard work ethic.

About the Authors

Kobe Nhin

Kobe loves to hang out with his brothers and dog, Bacon. He is a member of the National Junior Honor Society. Kobe is inspired to write to help others overcome any negative self beliefs that may hinder their growth as it did his. He has learned to develop a storm-chasing mindset, always looking for obstacles to overcome.

For lesson plans, visit **www.KobeNhin.com** and sign up for new book releases. Follow him on social media **f @MentalToughnessTips** **@GrowGrit**

Mary Nhin

Mary loves being the guinea pig for all her husband, Kang's kitchen creations. She is a mom of 3 boys, wife of 23 years, business/life coach, and author. For 20 years, she and Kang have been enriching people's lives through their companies Nhinja and Grow Grit Press. She has been awarded the Forty under 40 and Inc. 5000.

For lesson plans, visit **www.MaryNhin.com** and sign up for new book releases. Follow her on social media **f @marynhin** **@marynhin**

Mental Toughness Growth Plan

I rate myself the following: 1-10 (10 is best)

	Today's Date:	Goal Date:
Example	6	9
Confidence		
Calm		
Carefree		
Motivated		
Focused		

Techniques I'm good at:

_____
_____
_____
_____
_____

Techniques I want to improve:

_____
_____
_____
_____
_____

Notes:

_____
_____
_____
_____
_____
_____

Positive Self-Talk

I am strong, confident and calm when I compete.
I can and will reach my highest goals.
I love to compete.

I use rituals.
I believe in myself and that I can reach my dreams.

Can you think of some more? Write them down here.

_____

_____

_____

_____

Rituals

Towel off between points.   Bounce on balls of your toes.   Touch the grass.   Tape your shin guards.

What rituals can you think of?

_____

_____

_____

_____

Mantras

Right here!   Let's do this!   On your toes   Fast feet!   Keep your head on a swivel!

What mantras can you think of?

_____

_____

_____

_____

Long-Term Goals (Motivation)

What are your long term goals?

_____

_____

_____

_____

What would be the worst thing that could happen if you didn't achieve this?

_____

_____

_____

_____

Number and list some short-term goals.

_____

_____

_____

_____

Now number and list an exercise or task that you could do on a regular basis for you to reach each short-term goal.

_____

_____

_____